The Ant and the Dove

retold by Sara Stuart
illustrated by John Wallner

Table of Contents

Chapter 1
Dove Helps Ant

On a bright, clear day, Ant went for a long, long walk. Soon he became thirsty and needed something to drink. So he went to find a stream. It was a stream that he had never been to before.

Slowly Ant walked down to the bank of the stream. He heard the water rushing along. Ant carefully leaned over and began to sip the cool water. He was so happy to taste the refreshing water.

Though Ant was careful, before he knew it, he had lost his balance. He was swept off the bank and fell into the cold, rushing stream.

Ant was terribly frightened because he had never learned to swim. He paddled his six tiny legs as quickly as he could. He tried so hard to stay afloat.

What could he do? He knew that if something did not happen soon, he would definitely drown.

Dove was sitting on a tree branch above the stream. From there she could see what was happening. She saw that Ant was in terrible trouble and knew that she must do something with haste.

Dove thought fast. Then she plucked a
large leaf from the tree. She dropped
it gently and watched the leaf fall into
the stream. Luckily, the leaf landed
right by Ant, just as Dove had hoped
it would.

Ant saw the leaf floating nearby. He climbed onto the leaf and rode the leaf to the bank of the stream. There he was safe once again.

Ant looked up and told Dove, "Thank you for saving me. I have never been so happy."

Then Ant began his walk home. As Ant walked, he heard loud footsteps and a rustling noise. He looked and saw a bird catcher.

Chapter 2
Ant Helps Dove

Ant glared at the man who was starting to build a trap with twigs. Ant knew that the trap was for Dove.

Ant crept closer and closer. Ant knew that Dove would fall right into the trap if Ant did not do something. So Ant crawled onto the bird catcher's leg and stung him with all his might.

The sting made the bird catcher throw up his arms. The twigs he was holding went flying into the air. And the bird catcher ran off.

The sudden noise made by the
scattered twigs alarmed Dove. She
flew away from her spot in the tree.

As Dove soared, she looked down to see what had made the noise. She saw the man running away. She saw the twigs scattered on the ground.

Dove understood what had happened.

Chapter 3
Friends

Dove swooped down
and landed next to Ant.

"Thank you for saving me.
I have never been so happy,"
Dove told Ant.

Then Dove flapped her wings
and flew away. And she
looked back and smiled.

Comprehension Check

Retell the Story

Use a Beginning, Middle, and End Chart to retell the story.

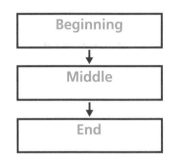

Think and Compare

I. How did the story end?

2. Ant and Dove both did something for each other. Tell about a time you did something good for someone.

3. Why is it important for people to be helpful to each other?